THIS BOOK BELONGS TO

....

This edition published by Parragon Books Ltd in 2016

Parragon Books Ltd
Chartist House
15–17 Trim Street
Bath BA1 1HA, UK
www.parragon.com

Superman created by Jerry Siegel and Joe Shuster.
By special arrangement with the Jerry Siegel company.

ISBN 978-1-4748-4473-4

Printed in Poland

SUPERMAN

ANNUAL 2017

UP, UP, AND AWAY!

SUPERMAN

THE STORY SO FAR....

Born as Kal-El on the planet Krypton.

Sent to Earth by his parents when Krypton explodes.

Crash lands in Smallville, Kansas, in the USA.

Adopted by Jonathan and Martha Kent who call him Clark.

Discovers he has superpowers.

Moves to Metropolis.

Takes a reporting job at the *Daily Planet*.

Meets fellow reporter Lois Lane.

Becomes Superman, Defender of Earth.

Keeps his identity secret from (almost) everyone.

SUPERMAN

Real name: Kal-El

Place of birth: Krypton

Occupation: Defender of Earth

Birth parents: Jor-El (father), Lara (mother)

Strengths: Super-strength, heat vision, super-speed, X-ray vision, flight, freezing breath, super-hearing

Weaknesses: Kryptonite

In his own words: "This looks like a job for Superman!"

DID YOU KNOW?

Superman gets his powers from Earth's yellow sun.

SUPERMAN'S SECRET!

When he's not saving the world, the Man Of Steel (as he's also known) works at the *Daily Planet* newspaper. Except nobody – not even Lois Lane – knows this. That's because Superman has a secret identity: the reporter, Clark Kent.

SUPERMAN IN ACTION ...

Superman is so strong that he can pick up tanks and other heavy objects with ease.

ODD HERO OUT

Which of these pictures of Superman is different from the others?

1

2

3

4

5

ANSWER ON PAGE 69

TO THE RESCUE

Superman needs your help to save the day. Lend him a hand by solving these challenges.

PERILOUS PATHS

Metropolis is under attack. Help Superman reach the city before it's reduced to rubble by choosing the correct route.

1

2

3

FINISH!

MULTIPLE MAYHEM

Superman's super-vision has gone crazy. How many times does the *Daily Planet* globe appear in this picture?

NAME GAME

Can you think of eight words to describe Superman starting with each of the letters in his name?

S ....
U ....
P ....
E ....
R ....
M ....
A ....
N ....

MYSTERY VILLAIN

Which fearsome foe is Superman fighting? Use your imagination to finish the picture.

ANATOMY OF A SUPER HERO

With his superhuman abilities, the Man Of Steel is almost indestructible. Super-villains beware!

X-RAY VISION

Superman can see through walls and other solid objects.

SUPER-HEARING

This awesome super hero can hear even the smallest sounds from great distances away.

FREEZING BREATH

Superman can freeze people and objects by breathing on them.

HEAT VISION

The Man Of Steel is able to melt things just by looking at them.

FLIGHT

Krypton's last son has the ability of true flight, which means he can soar to the rescue whenever danger strikes.

DID YOU KNOW?

Superman has a secret home in the Arctic. It's called the Fortress Of Solitude.

SUPER-SPEED

Faster than the speed of light, Superman is so quick, he can cross our entire solar system in a matter of minutes.

INVULNERABILITY

It is very difficult to harm Superman, unless he is weakened by Kryptonite.

SUPER-STRENGTH

The Man Of Steel is incredibly strong. He can crush diamonds with his hands, mountains and move planets.

S-SHIELD SCRAMBLE

Superman's famous S-Shield is missing some pieces. Draw lines between the missing parts and the matching shapes until you have completed the puzzle.

PROFILE:

LEX LUTHOR

Real name: Alexander Joseph Luthor

Place of birth: Metropolis

Occupation: CEO of LexCorp, billionaire businessman, criminal mastermind

Parents: Lionel and Letitia Luthor

Strengths: Supreme intellect, vast amounts of money, political influence

Weaknesses: His pride and arrogance

In his own words: "Metropolis is mine!"

LUTHOR IN ACTION ...

Lex once attempted to take over Metropolis using a powerful laser. Thankfully, Superman was on hand to thwart his evil plan.

DID YOU KNOW?

When Lex Luthor first appeared in the Superman comic he had a full head of red hair.

MIND GAMES

Outwit the mighty Lex Luthor by completing these baffling brainteasers.

MEMORY TEST

Look carefully at these words, all describing Lex Luthor, then cover them up and see how many you can remember.

INVENTOR	MASTERMIND	CRIMINAL
BUSINESSMAN	BALD	RICH
GENIUS	VILLAIN	SCIENTIST

DOUBLE TROUBLE

Can you find five differences between the billionaire businessman and his mirror image?

NEMESIS BY NUMBERS

Join the dots to reveal Lex's greatest enemy!

EYE SPY

Lex has lost his Kryptonite ring. Look closely at this picture ... can you spot where he dropped it?

LAST SON OF KRYPTON

KAL-EL ROCKETED TO EARTH AS A BABY JUST BEFORE HIS PLANET KRYPTON DIED. WHEN A FARMING COUPLE FOUND HIM, THEY NAMED HIM CLARK KENT. BUT THIS NEWS REPORTER HAS A SECRET IDENTITY. HE IS ... SUPERMAN!

AS SUPERMAN HE REPRESENTS FAIRNESS, HONOUR AND, ABOVE ALL, FEARLESSNESS IN THE FACE OF DANGER.

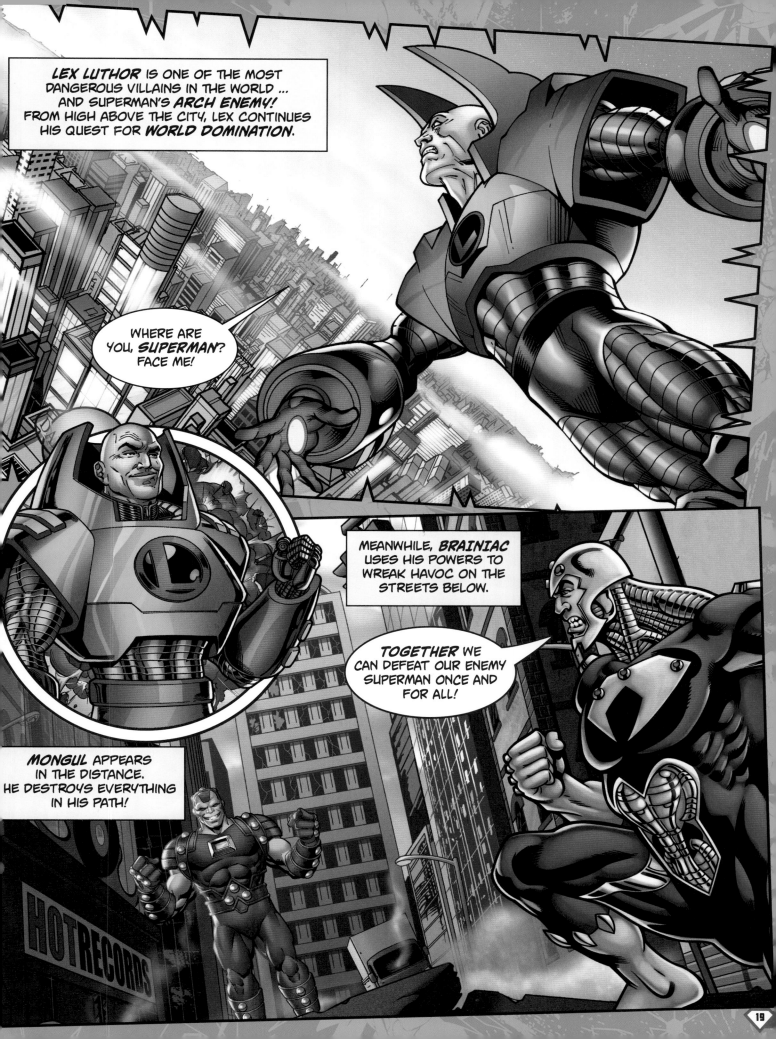

FEARED THROUGHOUT THE COSMOS, MONGUL IS A WALKING *ENGINE OF DESTRUCTION* AND A REAL MATCH FOR SUPERMAN!

RUN, PATHETIC HUMANS!

SUPERMAN IS IN THE *FORTRESS OF SOLITUDE....*

THERE'S *TROUBLE IN METROPOLIS!*

WHOOSH!

DRAW SUPERMAN

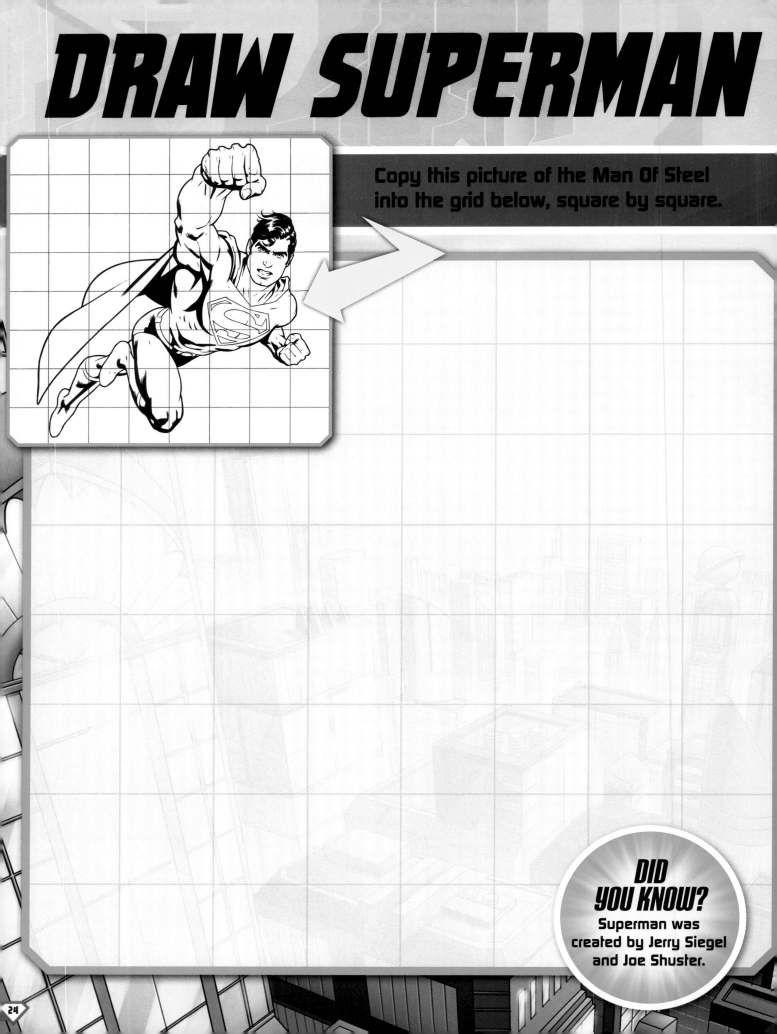

Copy this picture of the Man Of Steel into the grid below, square by square.

DID YOU KNOW?

Superman was created by Jerry Siegel and Joe Shuster.

MAN of STEEL WORD SEARCH

Find the words at the bottom of the page in the grid below. Answers can run forwards, backwards, up, down and diagonally. Good luck!

```
T Y A D I J J J K F R E P U S D
O P D E A B U A W S A D T O I Y
B R A V E D S P F D A U T L R A
H D E R T E T Y P B S R A S H H
G A L O U E I X L A U A A Q A E
A D A K A I C W A T E I A D S R
A V B F R R E T H T L X R Y R O
F D Q D C Y E W S A A F B P L U
O F T B V Q P W D P O G L R P F
R U E O I U A T A K R D T O V C
T O P P J P C L O A T F A T R G
R P A P V Z X E W N K D F E Y N
E K C A I H D Z D G O C V C I O
S N C G P L A U S A F D Y T O R
S A E L L I V L L A M S A O P T
Y T A U Y O E A C H V J A R L S
```

HERO   BRAVE
KRYPTON   TRUTH
SUPER   FORTRESS
CAPE   JUSTICE
PROTECTOR   ALIAS
SMALLVILLE   STRONG

DRESS LIKE CLARK KENT

To all but a few of his friends, Clark Kent is an ordinary reporter for the *Daily Planet*. But he has a secret. Underneath those glasses is a super hero-in-waiting. Transform yourself into Superman's alter-ego by following the instructions below.

YOU WILL NEED:

- Safety scissors
- Thin card
- Glue
- Safety pins

INSTRUCTIONS

1. Glue these pages to a piece of thin card.

2. Wait until the glue is dry then carefully cut out Clark's glasses, tie, S-Shield and Press Pass along the dotted lines.

3. Bend the glasses into shape and tuck the tie into your collar. Fasten the S-Shield under your shirt using safety pins and have your Press Pass ready. You are good to go!

Scissors and safety pins can be dangerous foes so ask an adult for help with this task.

DAILY PLANET

PRESS PASS

Clark Kent

Investigative Reporter

Clark Kent

DID YOU KNOW?
To prevent people finding out his real identity, Superman wears glasses when he's disguised as Clark. He also changes his mannerisms so that no one guesses who he really is.

PROFILE:

LOIS LANE

DID YOU KNOW?
Lois has a younger sister named Lucy Lane.

Real name: Lois Lane

Place of birth: Ramstein Air Base

Occupation: Award-winning journalist for the *Daily Planet*

Parents: Samuel and Elenor Lane

Strengths: Ambitious, street smart, gutsy, intelligent, hard-working

Weaknesses: Lois's nose for a story often lands her in trouble

In her own words: "I'll tell you what that is. It's our front-page story. Let's go."

LOIS IN ACTION ...

Lois is very brave and will stop at nothing to get a front-page scoop, even if it means putting her life in danger.

JIMMY OLSEN

James Bartholomew Olsen (better known as Jimmy) is a photojournalist for the *Daily Planet*. He's bright and very eager and is a loyal friend to both Superman and Clark Kent.

DID YOU KNOW?
Jimmy owns a wristwatch that can signal Superman anywhere on Earth.

BIZARRO

Bizarro is Superman's doppelganger and is more trouble than he's worth ... most of the time. Every once in a while, however, he helps out the Man Of Steel ... in his own bizarre way.

DID YOU KNOW?
Bizarro lives in Bizarro World, a place where everything is backwards and the opposite of how it is on Earth.

KRYPTO

Krypto is Superman's super-dog. He possesses many of the same powers as the Man Of Steel including flight, super-strength and super-speed. He lives in the Fortress Of Solitude and wears a red cape.

DID YOU KNOW?
Krypto was given to Kal-El when he was a baby.

FRIENDS IN NEED

Team up with Lois, Jimmy, Krypto and Bizarro to conquer these tricky puzzles....

LOOK OUT, LOIS!
The *Daily Planet*'s hot-shot reporter has found herself in the middle of a fierce battle between Mongul and Superman. Finish the picture by adding some colour.

EXTREME CLOSE-UP

Jimmy is having problems with the zoom lens on his camera. Can you work out who the young photographer has been taking pictures of?

A

B

C

D

BACK TO FRONT ANAGRAMS

Everything is backwards in Bizarro's world, including these anagrams. You'll need a mirror to read them! Then rearrange the letters to spell out the names of some of Superman's closest allies.

A YOL MILS NEM

B NOIL ƎLAƧ

C TЯAK MƎHTИA

D TAB ИAM

E ИƎЯW ИAMDOOW

SHADOW HUNTER!

Superman's heroic dog is one of a kind – and this puzzle proves it. Only one silhouette exactly matches the picture of Krypto. Can you spot which one?

A **B** **C**

D

E

EXTRA! EXTRA! Did you know that Lois Lane once had her own best-selling comic book series? It was called *Superman's Girl Friend Lois Lane* and ran for 137 issues.

ANSWERS ON PAGE 69

READ ALL ABOUT IT

DAILY PLANET™

Superman has made the front page of the *Daily Planet* again, but it's up to you to decide why. Write an exciting story about the Man Of Steel below, then draw a picture to go with it.

WHEN YOU'RE WRITING YOUR STORY, REMEMBER TO ASK YOURSELF THE QUESTIONS IN THE BOX BELOW.

WHO is it about?
WHAT happened?
WHEN did it happen?
WHERE did it happen?
WHY did it happen?

SPOT THE DIFFERENCE

No two days are ever the same at the *Daily Planet*. There's always an exciting story unfolding, usually about Superman. Look carefully at these two pictures of Clark, Lois and Jimmy at work and see if you can find 10 differences between them.

DID YOU KNOW?

Superman couldn't always fly. When the character was first introduced, he was only able to leap over tall buildings.

ANSWERS ON PAGE 69

RACE AGAINST TIME

Krypto arrives to help you. Take another turn.

YOU WILL NEED:

- Safety scissors
- Six-sided die
- Three friends to play with

CUT OUT THESE COUNTERS

HOW TO PLAY:

1. Pick a counter each and place them on START.

2. Roll the die one by one. The player with the highest number goes first.

3. Take turns to move around the board. Do your best to land on the booster spaces, but try to avoid the ones that will slow you down.

4. The first player to reach the *Daily Planet* building is the winner.

START

Change from Clark Kent into Superman. Move forward three spaces.

Soar up, up and away. Fly forward four spaces.

Stop to help Jimmy. Miss a go.

PROFILE:

BATMAN

Real name: Bruce Wayne

Place of birth: Crest Hill, Gotham City

Occupation: Billionaire businessman, crime fighter

Parents: Thomas and Martha Wayne

Strengths: Brilliant detective, supreme athlete and martial artist, hugely wealthy

Weaknesses: Walks the line between light and dark

In his own words: "To the Batmobile!"

BATMAN IN ACTION ...

Batman has a huge collection of hi-tech weapons and gadgets, which he uses to protect the people of Gotham City – and occasionally, Metropolis.

DID YOU KNOW?

Batman lives in an enormous mansion called Wayne Manor.

The Batmobile

Night Vision Binoculars

Underwater Breathing Device

Grappling Hook

WONDER WOMAN

Real name: Diana Of Themyscira

Place of birth: Paradise Island (also known as Themyscira)

Occupation: Government agent, ambassador, warrior princess of the Amazons

Parents: Zeus (father), Hippolyta (mother)

Strengths: Super-speed, flight, great wisdom

Weaknesses: Vulnerable to piercing weapons such as arrows and swords

In her own words:
"Great Hera!"

DID YOU KNOW?
Wonder Woman's most prized possession is her golden lasso. Anyone she captures with it is forced to tell the truth. She also has an Invisible Jet.

WONDER WOMAN IN ACTION ...
Wonder Woman's trademark bulletproof bracelets combined with her incredible speed mean she can fend off almost any attack.

SAVING THE DAY

Superman may be almost indestructible but even he needs a little help from his super hero pals now and then. Swing into action with Batman and Wonder Woman by solving these crafty puzzlers....

① ② ③ ④ ⑤ ⑥ ⑦

BATMOBILE MIX-UP

Help Batman put his Batmobile back together by writing the correct order into the spaces below.

MOMENT OF TRUTH

Wonder Woman has Darkseid in a twist but which lasso will lead her to him?

① ② ③

MAZE DAZE

Superman is trapped. Help Batman get through the maze to free him.

DID YOU KNOW?

Wonder Woman was trained to fight by Ares, the God Of War.

JETTING AROUND

Join the dots to see Wonder Woman's favourite way of travelling.

SPOT THE BATARANGS

How many Batarangs can you find on these two pages?

FILL IN THE BLANKS

Lois Lane's laptop has been infected with a virus and it's made some of the words in her story disappear. Can you help the *Daily Planet*'s prize-winning reporter salvage her work before her editor Perry White finds out? Use the list below to help you — each word appears in the report only once.

SUPERMAN TO THE _____

The City Of _____ almost became a thing of the past today when an _____ suffered catastrophic engine _____ . The plane, which was carrying 200 people including billionaire businessman Lex _____, lost power over Queensland Park Borough, near Metropolis Harbor, and began _____ towards the S.T.A.R. Labs research facility.

    With disaster looming, Superman arrived in the nick of time to save the _____ . The Man Of Steel plucked the aircraft out of the _____ and landed it gently in the research facility's car _____ . No one was _____ .

    "I thought I was a goner for sure," said one relieved _____ . "Superman is my hero!"

    Lex Luthor declined to _____ .

HURT
FALLING
DAY
RESCUE
PARK
FAILURE

AIRLINER
LUTHOR
PASSENGER
COMMENT
TOMORROW
SKY

SUPERMAN SUDOKU

To defeat villains such as Lex Luthor, Superman needs brains as well as brawn. Put your wits to the test by completing these challenging picture puzzles.

HOW TO PLAY:

Fill in the blanks so that each row, column and square has one of each character. You can always write their names if drawing them is too tricky.

DID YOU KNOW?

The S in Superman's S-Shield doesn't stand for Superman. It's the crest of Kal-El's family and means 'hope'.

ANSWERS ON PAGE 69

53

TEST YOUR SUPERMAN KNOWLEDGE

Do you know your Krypto from your Kryptonite? Tick your answers and let's find out....

I WILL RULE THIS CITY!

1. Who created the character of Superman?

A Jerry Siegel and Joe Shuster ▽
B Bob Kane and Bill Finger ▽
C William Moulton Marston ▽

2. Where was Superman born?

A Smallville ▽
B Krypton ▽
C Gotham City ▽

3. What is Superman's alien name?

A Kal-El ▽
B Jor-El ▽
C Clark Kent ▽

4. Who is Superman's alias?

A Bruce Wayne ▽
B Kent Clark ▽
C Clark Kent ▽

5. What is the source of Superman's powers?

A Earth's yellow sun
B His suit
C Government experiments

6. What is Superman's biggest weakness?

A Silver
B Fire
C Kryptonite

7. Which of the following isn't a Superman power?

A Shrinking
B X-ray vision
C Super-speed

8. What is Superman also known as?

A The Man Of Steel
B The Caped Crusader
C The Blue And Scarlet Speedster

9. What is the name of Superman's loyal dog?

A Comet
B Krypto
C Beppo

10. Who is Superman's main enemy?

A Perry White
B The Joker
C Lex Luthor

11. What is the name of Superman's secret hideaway in the Arctic?

A The Citadel Of Remoteness
B The Fortress Of Solitude
C The Castle Of Peace And Quiet

12. Which newspaper does Clark Kent write for?

A The Daily Planet
B Metropolis Today
C Earth Times

13. What does the 'S' on Superman's shield stand for?

A Truth
B Justice
C Hope

14. Which of the following is not an ally of Superman's?

A Lois Lane
B Jimmy Olsen
C Mongul

15. What is the name of Superman's doppelganger?

A Bizarro
B Superman 2.0
C Mansuper

NOT ON MY WATCH, LUTHOR!

HOW DID YOU DO?

1-5: TRY AGAIN!
6-10: MIGHTY EFFORT!
11-15: SUPERPOWERED!

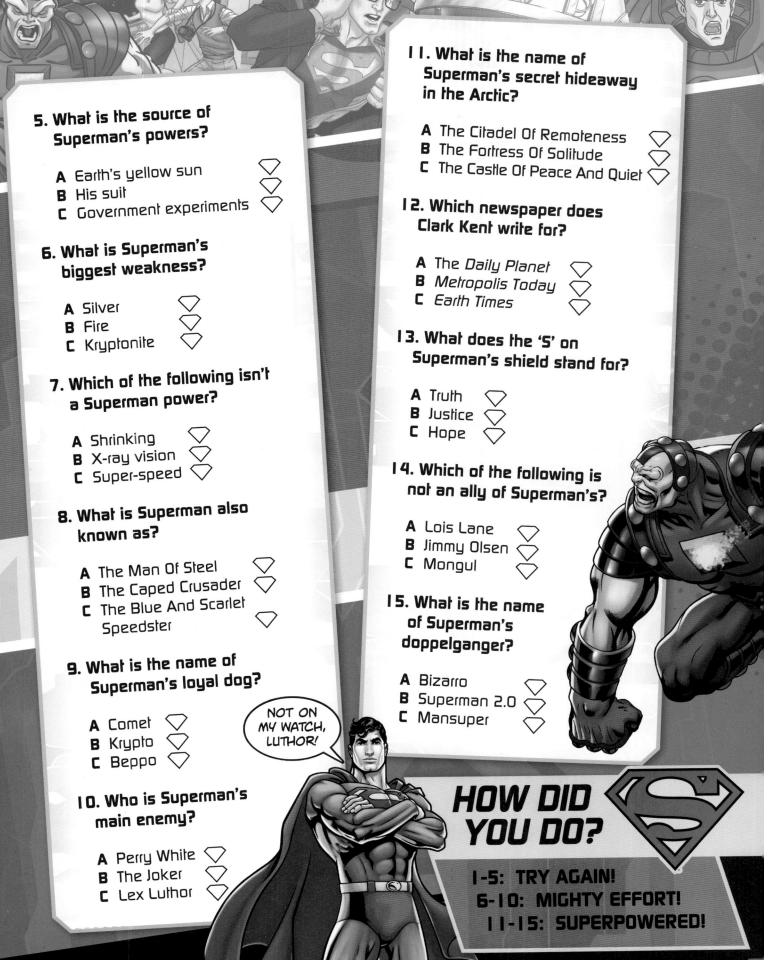

PROFILE:

DOOMSDAY

One of Superman's deadliest enemies, Doomsday was brought to life on Krypton by a mad alien scientist who wanted to create the ultimate hunter. He is the perfect killing machine and leaves a trail of destruction wherever he goes.

FEARSOME FACT: Every time Doomsday is defeated, he comes back more powerful than before.

BRAINIAC

Nicknamed the 'Collector Of Worlds', Brainiac is a supremely intelligent alien from the planet Colu. He tours the universe gathering information about everyone and everything he comes across, which he then uses for his own evil ends.

FEARSOME FACT: Brainiac has a spacecraft in the shape of a skull. It's known as the Skull Ship.

MONGUL

Mongul used to rule an alien world but he was so cruel that his citizens rebelled against him and banished him into space. Now he travels the cosmos looking to conquer other planets. He is extremely cunning and incredibly strong.

FEARSOME FACT: Mongul is nearly 2.5 metres tall.

DARKSEID

Darkseid is the evil ruler of Apokolips. He has one goal ... to conquer the entire universe. As well as being incredibly strong and intelligent, he is able to shoot Omega Beams from his eyes. These beams are made up of powerful bio-electric energy and will destroy almost anything in their path.

FEARSOME FACT: Darkseid travels through time and space using a device known as a Mother Box.

SUPER-VILLAIN

START

Lois and Jimmy are in trouble and only Superman can save them! Help the Man Of Steel reach his friends, avoiding Doomsday, Brainiac, Darkseid, Mongul and Lex Luthor along the way!

MEGA MAZE

FINISH

WHICH SUPERMAN CHARACTER ARE YOU?

Tick your answers to the questions below and let's find out!

1. What's your favourite type of film?

a) Science fiction
b) Animal adventure
c) Super hero flick
d) Home movie
e) Anything with bad guys

2. Where are you when trouble strikes?

a) Saving the day
b) Ready and willing to help
c) In the thick of the action
d) Observing from a distance
e) I'm usually the cause of the trouble

3. What's your biggest fear?

a) Letting down those who depend on me
b) Missing dinner
c) Forgetting to turn in my homework
d) Being treated like I'm invisible
e) Being outwitted

4. Which word best describes you?

a) Strong
b) Loyal
c) Determined
d) Enthusiastic
e) Ambitious

5. Your bedroom is filled with ...

a) Dressing-up clothes
b) Toys
c) Newspaper cuttings
d) Photographs
e) The latest gadgets

NOW ADD UP YOUR ANSWERS....

MOSTLY As
YOU ARE ... SUPERMAN

Like Superman, you're the first person your friends turn to when they're in trouble. You're brave and resourceful and always willing to lend a hand to those in need. Just remember to make time for yourself now and then.

MOSTLY Bs
YOU ARE ... KRYPTO

Like Krypto, you are devoted to your family and friends. You don't tend to say much, but when you do bark (we mean talk), people listen. You have a playful side and love to have fun.

MOSTLY Cs
YOU ARE ... LOIS LANE

Like Lois, once you set your mind to something there's absolutely no stopping you. You love to find things out and always give 100 per cent in everything you do. Whatever path you take, a promising future awaits.

MOSTLY Ds
YOU ARE ... JIMMY OLSEN

Like Jimmy, you're eager and hardworking and you never take no for an answer. Whenever there's a setback, you just shrug your shoulders and try, try again. You prefer getting out and about to being stuck indoors.

MOSTLY Es
YOU ARE ... LEX LUTHOR

Like Lex, you're bursting with brains and ideas. Despite your cool exterior, you worry a lot about what others think of you. There's no doubt you're destined for big things – just make sure it's not at the expense of your friends and family.

---

6. What's your personal motto?

a) Truth, justice ... all that stuff ▽
b) Friends to the end ▽
c) Hard work never hurt anyone ▽
d) If at first you don't succeed, try, try again ▽
e) Play to win ▽

7. Your ideal home is ...

a) A quiet retreat far from anywhere ▽
b) Warm and dry ▽
c) A swanky city apartment ▽
d) Whatever I can afford ▽
e) A hi-tech mansion ▽

8. What's your dream job?

a) Pilot ▽
b) Celebrity sidekick ▽
c) Journalist ▽
d) Photographer ▽
e) Businessman ▽

FEARLESS FUNNIES

In times of crisis, it's good to laugh. Try out these gravity-defying gigglers on your friends.

What do you get if you cross the Man Of Steel with a bowl of broth?

Souperman!

Why did Lois Lane's laptop go to the doctor?

It had a virus.

What does Superman like in his drink?

Just ice.

What's black and white and read all over?

The *Daily Planet*.

What's Superman's favourite part of a joke?

The punch line.

Why can't the Man Of Steel go swimming?

He gets rusty.

What do you get if you cross Lex Luthor with a biro?

A bald point pen.

What's Superman's favourite drink?

Fruit punch.

ANSWERS

Page 9

ODD HERO OUT
Superman 4 is missing his belt buckle

Page 10

PERILOUS PATHS
Path 2

MULTIPLE MAYHEM
There are 20 *Daily Planet* globes

Page 14

S-SHIELD SCRAMBLE
A – 3, B – 5, C – 7, D – 1, E – 6,
F – 2, G– 4

Pages 16–17

DOUBLE TROUBLE

EYE SPY

NEMESIS BY NUMBERS
Lex's greatest enemy is Superman!

Page 25

MAN OF STEEL WORD SEARCH

```
T Y A D I J J J K F R E P U S D
O P D E A B U A W S A D T O I Y
B R A V E D S P F D A U T L R A
H D E R T E T Y P B S R A S H H
G A L O U E I X L A U A A Q A E
A D A K A I C W A T E I A D S R
A V B F R R E T H T L X R Y H O
F D Q D C Y E W S A A F B P L U
O F T B V O P W D P O G L R P F
R U E O I U A T A K R D T O V C
T O P P J P C L O A T F A T R G
R P A P V Z X E W N K D F E Y N
E K C A I H D Z D G O C V L S O
S N C G P L A U S A F D Y T R R
S A E L L I V L L A M S A O P L
Y T A U Y O E A C H V J A R L S
```

Page 31

EXTREME CLOSE-UP
A – Clark Kent
B – Superman
C – Krypto
D – Bizarro

BACK TO FRONT ANAGRAMS
A – Jimmy Olsen
B – Lois Lane
C – Martha Kent
D – Batman
E – Wonder Woman

SHADOW HUNTER!
The correct Krypto is A

Page 39

SPOT THE DIFFERENCE

Pages 44–45

BATMOBILE MIX-UP
3, 2, 6, 4, 1, 7, 5

MOMENT OF TRUTH
Lasso 3

MAZE DAZE

JETTING AROUND
Wonder Woman's favourite way of travelling is in her Invisible Jet plane!

SPOT THE BATARANGS
There are 12 Batarangs

Pages 52–53

FILL IN THE BLANKS
SUPERMAN TO THE **RESCUE**
The City Of **Tomorrow** almost became a thing of the past today when an **airliner** suffered catastrophic engine **failure**. The plane, which was carrying 200 people including billionaire businessman Lex **Luthor**, lost power over Queensland Park Borough, near Metropolis Harbor, and began **falling** towards the S.T.A.R. Labs research facility.

With disaster looming, Superman arrived in the nick of time to save the **day**. The Man Of Steel plucked the aircraft out of the **sky** and landed it gently in the research facility's car **park**. No one was **hurt**.

"I thought I was a goner for sure," said one relieved **passenger**. "Superman is my hero!"

Lex Luthor declined to **comment**.

SUPERMAN SUDOKU

Pages 54–55

TEST YOUR SUPERMAN KNOWLEDGE
1 – A, 2 – B, 3 – A, 4 – C, 5 – A, 6 – C, 7 – A, 8 – A, 9 – B, 10 – C, 11 – B, 12 – A, 13 – C, 14 – C, 15 – A

Pages 58–59

SUPER-VILLAIN MEGA MAZE